Come gather 'round people
where-ever you roam
and admit that the
waters around you have grown
and accept it that
soon you'll be drenched
to the bone,
if your time to you
is worth savin'
then you better start swimmin'
or you'll sink like a stone,
for the times they are a-changin'.

bob
dylan

SONG BOOK

M. WITMARK & SONS, NEW YORK, N.Y.   •   PHOTOGRAPHS BY CHUCK STEWART   •   PRICE $4.95 IN U.S.A.

TABLE of CONTENTS

FIRST LINE • INDEX

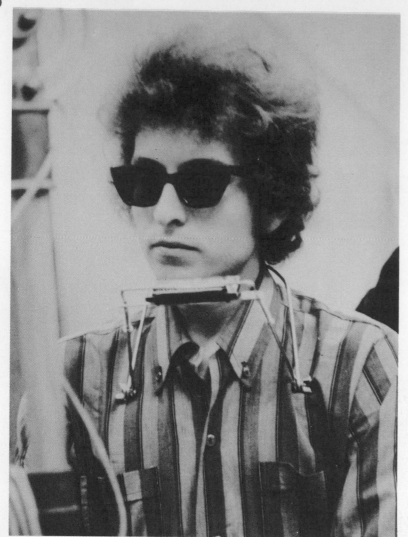

dylan recording

personal notes

"Winter time in New York town,
The wind blowin', snow around,
Walk around with no where to go
Somebody could freeze right to the bone.
I froze right to the bone."

(*From "Talkin' New York" by Bob Dylan*)

That was in the winter of 1961. Dylan was only 20 years old, but he had already sung his way through half the states in the country. He'd run away to Chicago when he was 10, travelled with a Texas carnival when he was 13, and thumbed his way for the next seven years from New Mexico to South Dakota, from Kansas to California. He'd come a long way East, mainly to visit the legendary Woody Guthrie, lying ill in a New Jersey hospital. A few months later, Dylan's raw-edged voice and the powerful imagery of his words had thrown the clan of folk music enthusiasts who gather at Gerde's Folk City in Greenwich Village into an uproar.

"He may," wrote Robert Shelton in the New York *Times*, "mumble the text of 'House of the Rising Sun' in a scarcely understandable growl or sob, or clearly enunciate the poetic poignancy of a Blind Lemon Jefferson blues . . . but his music-making has the mark of originality and inspiration, all the more noteworthy for his youth. Mr. Dylan is vague about his antecedents and birthplace, but it matters less where he has been than where he is going, and that would seem to be straight up."

In the fall of the same year, Dylan walked into a Columbia Records studio to make his first album. Upon the release of the simply titled "Bob Dylan," the *Saturday Review* remarked that the record has presented "one of the most creative and communicative of folk artists since Woody Guthrie." The reception accorded Dylan's next albums, "The

Times They Are A-Changin'," "Another Side of Bob Dylan," "The Freewheelin' Bob Dylan" and "Bringing It All Back Home," "Highway 61 Revisited," has been overwhelming.

His have been the most favorably received appearances at both the Monterey and Newport Folk Festivals. The cities of Boston, Philadelphia, Ann Arbor, Washington and Chicago are awaiting return engagements, and his masterfully delivered program in the spring of 1963 at New York City's Town Hall resulted in one-man concerts at Carnegie Hall and Lincoln Center where stage seats were necessary to accommodate overflow audiences.

His impact has been equally as forceful throughout the world. The winner of two of Britain's most coveted national awards in 1964: Best Folk Music Record, for his album, "The Freewheelin' Bob Dylan," and Most Outstanding Newcomer to Records, the folk singer recently completed his second tour of England. His extended series of appearances in that country, climaxed by two concerts at London's famous Albert Hall, ended with his emergence as the most important new entertainer in all of Great Britain. His first four albums are currently in the top twenty listing of *Record Retailer*, Britain's leading music trade paper, and his singles, "The Times They Are A-Changin'" and "Subterranean Homesick Blues," are also climbing the charts. There is reason for such enthusiasm. For in the years since he came East, Bob Dylan—singer, composer, poet, humorist, spokesman—has developed into the most creative force in folk music today.

As folk poet, Bob Dylan is without peer among his generation. His songs or "stories," as he calls them, have been sung and recorded by Odetta, Marlene Dietrich, Peter, Paul and Mary, The Kingston Trio, Ian and Sylvia, The Chad Mitchell

Trio, Bobby Darin, Pete Seeger and Judy Collins. Joan Baez is preparing an album of all-Bob Dylan material. Many of his songs, such as "Don't Think Twice, It's All Right," "Blowin' in the Wind," "A Hard Rain's A-Gonna Fall" and "Masters of War," have been among the most popular recordings in the country. Their quality, however, has insured them a place in American music more permanent than a high listing on best-selling charts.

Dylan is a deeply committed young man who conveys his concern for the world around him through unique and poetic imagery that makes explicit the human condition. As critic Robert Shelton has noted, "Dylan breaks all the rules of songwriting except that of having something to say and saying it stunningly."

With a mussed shock of hair topping gaunt, sensitive features, dressed in beat-up blue jeans, boots and wrinkled shirts, Dylan appears an outlandish, Chaplinesque figure. He accompanies himself with a driving guitar and a harmonica that complements the sometimes bleak wail or guttural murmur of his voice. Moods of poignancy, anger, bitterness and hope have not been projected so movingly since the days of Leadbelly and Big Bill Broonzy. He has been influenced by them and by Hank Williams, Muddy Waters, Jelly Roll Morton, Mance Lipscomb and Big Joe Williams. His Midwestern twang, expert handling of the "talking blues" and sardonic wit seem almost directly traceable to Woody Guthrie.

Dylan is a compelling stylist in the tradition of those immortals, but his words are the impassioned poetry of now, and he sings them in his own highly individual and continually evolving manner.

The frenetic revival of folk music in this country has spawned the careers of legions of young singers, variously allied with the so-called ethnic, authentic, purist and urban-singer schools. Dylan is closest to the last, but, in fact, so distinctive in style that he defies classification. Rising above folk music as a vogue, he seizes the themes of loneliness, fear, war, freedom and despair, transcends their potentiality for tiresome cliche and, in a fusion of Negro blues and country music, translates them into a profound aesthetic experience. It is this that has led Pete Seeger to say that "He'll be America's greatest troubador" and to add, as if the younger singer's commitment were almost too intense, "if he doesn't explode."

Born in Duluth, Minnesota on May 24, 1941, Bob Dylan lived off and on for his first 17 years in Hibbing, Minnesota, a mining town "way up on the Canadian border." In an often hilarious summary of his early experiences called "My Life in a Stolen Minute," Dylan wrote, "Hibbing's a good ol' town. I ran away from it when I was 10, 12, 13, 15, 15½, 17 an' 18. I been caught an' brought back all but once."

His first jaunt was to Chicago and before the police found him, the 10-year-old runaway had gotten his first guitar from the friend of a street singer on the South Side. By age 15, he'd also taught himself piano, autoharp and harmonica and had written his first song, dedicated to Brigitte Bardot. Thereafter his restlessness took him to Gallup, New Mexico; Cheyenne, South Dakota; Sioux Falls, South Dakota ("I didn't learn songs there, just ways of singing"); Phillipsburg, Kansas, and Burbank, California ("That's where I first saw Woody"). Dylan graduated from high school in Hibbing and attended the University of Minnesota for a little less than six months, where he learned that "lots of people go to college."

"From God knows where," exclaimed a critic for the San Francisco *Examiner*, "Dylan has absorbed, engorged or engulfed all the techniques of the unlettered greats of the folk song tradition, including the rich strain of Negro contribution to the culture."

Dylan's explanation—"Open up your eyes an' ears an' yer influenced—an' there's nothing you can do about it . . . I just seem to draw into myself whatever comes my way and it comes out me."

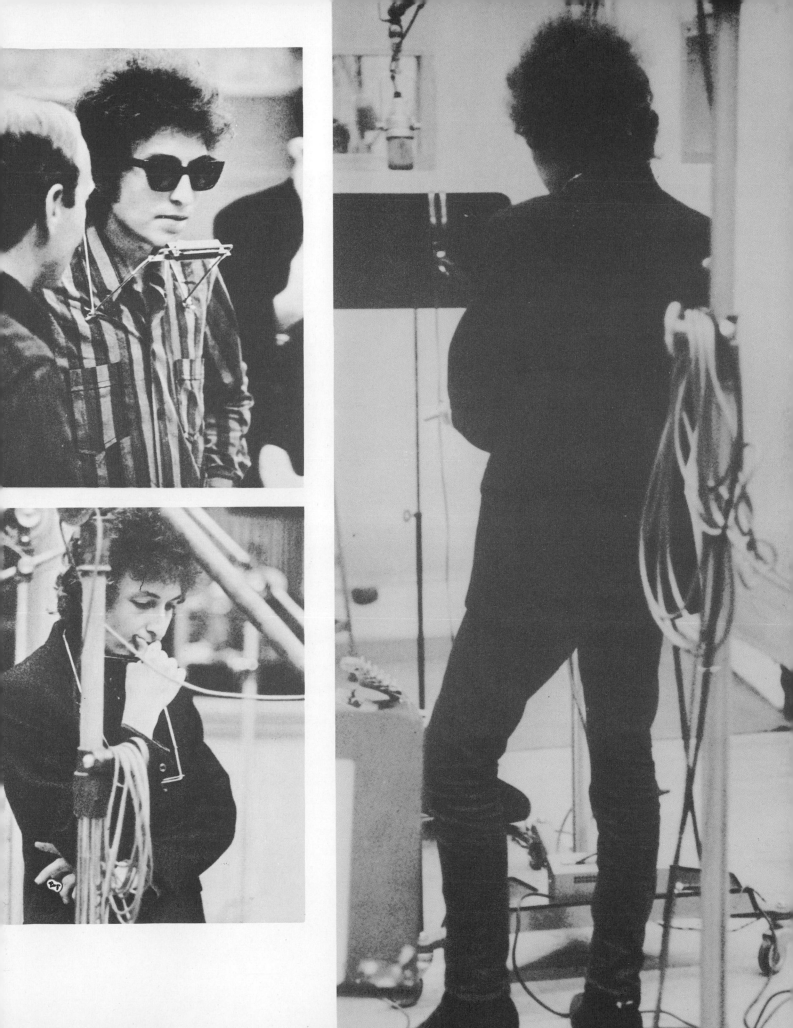

the man behind the songs

By Robert Shelton
(Folk music critic of The New York Times)

These are the songs of Bob Dylan, the pioneer, the trail-blazer, the innovator, who has disturbed, delighted, dismayed and deepened the thinking of millions of listeners. He breaks all the rules. He sets new compass-points. He experiments and assimilates all musical influences, then turns about to influence the musical worlds around him.

In the late summer of 1965 the national press again took cognizance of Dylan's importance. The *New York Times* and *Variety* both called him the most influential American writer-performer to emerge in a decade. *Newsweek* called him "the Patrick Henry of this (folk rock) revolution," while *Time* said: "Folk rock owes its origins to Bob Dylan, 24, folk music's most celebrated contemporary composer."

Folk rock was but one of a half-dozen styles that Dylan had run through in four years of professional performing and writing. Study the words and tunes herein and you will find a portrait of one of the musical-poetic geniuses of our time, an artist as multi-faceted as a Picasso or a Cocteau, running through new concepts with such a burning creativity that he often outruns the comprehension of his followers.

Who is this fountainhead of song? What is he really like? Not even the closest friends of Bob Dylan could agree on an answer. He keeps his own counsel and always has. They will tell you he hates lifelessness, hypocrisy, regimentation, injustice, pomposity. They will tell you that, although he loves to laugh and play outrageous jokes, he is somber often, tortured frequently, thinking always.

When Bob Dylan first arrived in New York, a callow, tousle-haired 19-year-old, he was writing comical-satirical talking blues songs. Then he moved into a deeper sort of comment about the world, railing as a poet against war in A HARD RAIN'S A GONNA FALL and MASTERS OF

WAR, against injustice in THE LONESOME DEATH OF HATTIE CARROLL. He deplored the effects of poverty in BALLAD OF HOLLIS BROWN and the profit made from suffering in WHO KILLED DAVEY MOORE? His TIMES THEY ARE A-CHANGIN' became a credo for the questioning, defiant collegiate generation that, for a time, elevated him to the role of spokesman.

Dylan was too individualistic an artist to wear the mantle of spokesman for anyone but himself. But like many another brilliant avant-garde creator, whenever he looked over his shoulder there were others following his lead. With BLOWIN' IN THE WIND his words entered the language of the integration movement. With MR. TAMBOURINE MAN, however, he announced his rejection of message over art and forecast new personalized directions. Then came SUBTERRANEAN HOMESICK BLUES and LIKE A ROLLING STONE, and Dylan's fantasy mind was driven by the high-voltage beat of folk rock.

The biography of Bob Dylan rests in his songs. His middle-class background, his leaving the University of Minnesota, his rambling around the country, his involvement in the Greenwich Village scene are mere details. . . . The thoughts and feelings of this turbulent talent are in his songs, some easily understood, some murkily symbolic with layers of meaning that do not emerge without repeated listening.

Here then is the musical biography of Bob Dylan, told in songs of love, songs of anger, songs of protest, songs of humor, songs of anguish, songs of hope, songs of the beauty and absurdity of the inner and outer world of which he writes.

Ballad of Hollis Brown

WORDS AND MUSIC BY BOB DYLAN

Moderato (in 4)

Refrain

1. He looked for work and mon-ey and he walked a rug-ged mile, ___

He looked for work and mon-ey and he walked a rug-ged mile. ___

Your chil-dren are so hun-gry that they

1-2-3 etc. (repeat for additional lyrics) | Last time   *Fine*

don't know how to smile. ___   2. Your

2. Your baby's eyes look crazy
    They're a tuggin' at your sleeve.
    Your baby's eyes look crazy
    They're a tuggin' at your sleeve.
    You walk the floor and wonder why
    With every breath you breathe.

3. The rats have got your flour
    Bad blood it got your mare.
    The rats have got your flour
    Bad blood it got your mare.
    Is there anyone that knows,
    Is there anyone that cares?

4. He prayed to the Lord above
    Oh please send you a friend.
    He prayed to the Lord above
    Oh please send you a friend.
    You ain' a got no money boy,
    You ain' a got no friend.

5. Your baby's eyes are crying louder
    It's pounding on your brain.
    Your babe is crying louder now
    It's pounding on your brain.
    Your wife's screams are stabbin'
    Like the dirty drivin' rain.

6. Your grass is turning black
    There's no water in your well.
    Your grass is turning black
    There's no water in your well.
    You spent your last long dollar
    On seven shot-gun shells.

7. Way out in the wilderness
    A cold coyote calls.
    Way out in the wilderness
    A cold coyote calls.
    Your eyes fix on a shot-gun
    That's hangin' on the wall.

8. Your brain is a bleedin'
    And your legs can't seem to stand.
    Your brain is a bleedin'
    And your legs can't seem to stand.
    Your eyes fix on the shot-gun
    That you're holdin' in your hand.

9. There's seven breezes a blowin'
    All around the cabin door.
    There's seven breezes a blowin'
    All around the cabin door.
    Seven shots sing out
    Like the ocean's pounding roar.

10. There's seven people dead
    On a South Dakota farm.
    There's seven people dead
    On a South Dakota farm.
    Somewhere in the distance
    There's seven new people born.

A Hard Rain's A Gonna Fall

WORDS AND MUSIC BY BOB DYLAN

Oh, where have you been, my blue-eyed son? Oh,

where have you been, my dar-ling young one?

1. I've

stum-bled on the side of__ twelve mis-ty moun-tains,
walked and I've crawled on__ six crook-ed high-ways,
stepped in the mid-dle of__ sev-en sad for-ests,
been out in front of a doz-en dead o-ceans,

2. I've
3. I've
4. I've

5. I've been ten thou-sand miles in the mouth of a grave-yard,

And it's a hard, and it's a hard, it's a

hard, and it's a hard, and it's a hard rain's

a gon-na fall.

D.S.

(A)   Oh, what did you see, my blue eyed son?
      Oh, what did you see, my darling young one?

(B)   I saw a new born baby with wild wolves all around it,
      I saw a highway of diamonds with nobody on it,
      I saw a black branch with blood that kept drippin',
      I saw a room full of men with their hammers a-bleedin',
      I saw a white ladder all covered with water,
      I saw ten thousand talkers whose tongues were all broken,

(C)   I saw guns and sharp swords in the hands of young children,
      And it's a hard, and it's a hard, it's a hard, it's a hard,
      And it's a hard rain's a gonna fall.

(A)   And what did you hear, my blue eyed son?
      And what did you hear, my darling young one?

(B)   I heard the sound of a thunder, it roared out a warnin',
      Heard the roar of a wave that could drown the whole world,
      Heard one hundred drummers whose hands were a blazin',
      Heard ten thousand whisperin' and nobody listenin',
      Heard one person starve, I heard many people laughin',
      Heard the song of a poet who died in the gutter,

(C)   Heard the sound of a clown who cried in the alley,
      And it's a hard, and it's a hard, it's a hard, it's a hard
      And it's a hard rain's a gonna fall.

(A)   Oh, who did you meet, my blue eyed son?
      Who did you meet, my darling young one?

(B)   I met a young child beside a dead pony,
      I met a white man who walked a black dog,
      I met a woman whose body was burning,
      I met a young girl, she gave me a rainbow,
      I met one man who was wounded in love,

(C)   I met another man who was wounded with hatred,
      And it's a hard, it's a hard, it's a hard, it's a hard
      It's a hard rain's a gonna fall.

(A)   Oh, what'll you do now, my blue eyed son?
      Oh, what'll you do now, my darling young one?

(B)   I'm a goin' back out 'fore the rain starts a fallin',
      I'll walk to the depth of the deepest black forest,
      Where the people are many and their hands are all empty,
      Where the pellets of poison are flooding their waters,
      Where the home in the valley meets the damp dirty prison,
      Where the executioner's face is always well hidden,
      Where hunger is ugly, where souls are forgotten,
      Where black is the color, where none is the number,
      And I'll tell it and think it and speak it and breathe it,
      And reflect it from the mountain so all souls can see it,
      Then I'll stand on the ocean until I start sinkin',

(C)   But I'll know my song well before I start singin',
      And it's a hard, it's a hard, it's a hard, it's a hard,
      It's a hard rain's a gonna fall.

Blowin' in the Wind

WORDS AND MUSIC BY BOB DYLAN

1. How man-y roads must a man walk down be-fore you
2. How man-y times must a man look up be-fore he can
3. How man-y years can a moun-tain ex-ist be-fore it's

call him a man? Yes, 'n' How man-y seas must a
see the sky? Yes, 'n' How man-y ears must
washed to the sea? Yes, 'n' How man-y years can some

white dove sail be-fore she sleeps in the sand? Yes, 'n'
one man have be-fore he can hear peo-ple cry? Yes, 'n'
peo-ple ex-ist be-fore they're al-lowed to be free? Yes, 'n'

Girl of the North Country

WORDS AND MUSIC BY BOB DYLAN

1. Well if you're trav-'lin' in the north coun-try fair, Where the winds hit heav-y on the bor-der-line, ___ Re-mem-ber me to

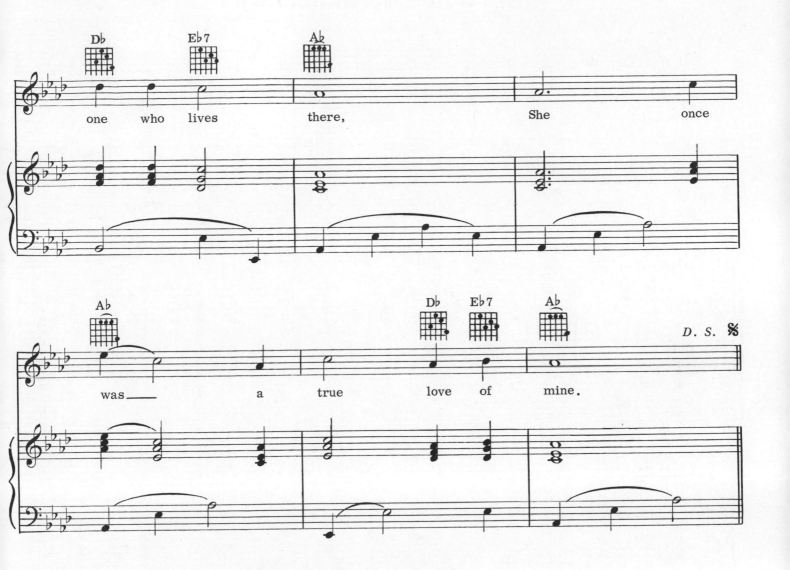

2. Well if you go in the snowflake storm
   When the rivers freeze and summer ends,
   Please see she has a coat so warm
   To keep her from the howlin' winds.

3. Please see for me if her hair hangs long,
   If it rolls and flows all down her breast,
   Please see for me her hair hangs long,
   That's the way I remember her best.

4. I'm a wonderin' if she remembers me at all,
   Many times I've often prayed
   In the darkness of my night,
   In the brightness of my day.

5. So if you're travelin' in the north country fair,
   Where the winds hit heavy on the borderline,
   Remember me to one who lives there,
   She once was a true love of mine.

Hero Blues

WORDS AND MUSIC BY BOB DYLAN

Bright

1. Yes — the gal I got I swear she's the scream - in' end
   go out and find some - bod - y to fight

She wants me to be a
She reads too man - y

he - ro so she can tell all her friends
books, she got new mov-ies in - side her head

Masters of War

WORDS AND MUSIC BY BOB DYLAN

walls   You that hide be-hind desks   I just

want you to   know I   can   see through your   masks   D.S. %

2. You that never done nothin'
   But build to destroy
   You play with my world
   Like it's your little toy
   You put a gun in my hand
   And you hide from my eyes
   And you turn and run farther
   When the fast bullets fly

3. Like Judas of old
   You lie and deceive
   A world war can be won
   You want me to believe
   But I see through your eyes
   And I see through your brain
   Like I see through the water
   That runs down my drain

4. You fasten the triggers
   For the others to fire
   Then you set back and watch
   When the death count gets higher
   You hide in your mansion
   As young people's blood
   Flows out of their bodies
   And is buried in the mud

5. You've thrown the worst fear
   That can ever be hurled
   Fear to bring children
   Into the world
   For threatenin' my baby
   Unborn and unnamed
   You ain't worth the blood
   That runs in your veins

6. How much do I know
   To talk out of turn
   You might say that I'm young
   You might say I'm unlearned
   But there's one thing I know
   Though I'm younger than you
   Even Jesus would never
   Forgive what you do

7. Let me ask you one question
   Is your money that good
   Will it buy you forgiveness
   Do you think that it could
   I think you will find
   When your death takes its toll
   All the money you made
   Will never buy back your soul

8. And I hope that you die
   And your death'll come soon
   I will follow your casket
   On a pale afternoon
   And I'll watch while you're lowered
   Down to your death bed
   And I'll stand o'er your grave
   Till I'm sure that you're dead.

Oxford Town

WORDS AND MUSIC BY BOB DYLAN

1. Ox-ford Town, Ox-ford Town, Ev-'ry-bod-y's got their heads bowed down, The sun don't shine a-bove the ground, Ain't a-go-in' down to Ox-ford Town.

2. He went down to Ox-ford Town, Guns and clubs fol-lowed him down,

34

Some - bod - y bet - ter in - ves - ti - gate soon.

6. Ox - ford Town, Ox - ford Town, Ev - 'ry - bod - y's got their

heads bowed down, The sun don't shine a - bove the ground,

Ain't a go - in' down to Ox - ford Town.

Tomorrow Is a Long Time

WORDS AND MUSIC BY BOB DYLAN

* ad lib quasi recitative

long time:___ Then lone-some would mean noth-ing to you__ at all; Yes, and
foot - steps;___ Or can't re-mem-ber the sound of my__ own name;
beau - ty ___ That I re-mem-ber in ___ my true love's eyes;

Refrain

on - ly if my own true love was wait-in'; _____ Yes, and if

I could hear her heart a-soft-ly pound-in'; _____ On-ly if she was ly-in'

by__ me:__ Then I'd lie in my bed once__ a-gain.

D.S. %

Walls of Red Wing

WORDS AND MUSIC BY BOB DYLAN

Oh, the age of the in-mates I re-mem-ber quite free-ly

No young-er than twelve, No old-er 'n sev-en-teen,

Thrown in like ban-dits And

cast off like crim-i-nals, In-side the

grounds 'Round the Walls of Red Wing.

D.S. %

2. From the dirty old mess hall
   You march to the brick wall,
   Too weary to talk
   And too tired to sing,
   Oh it's all afternoon
   You remember your home town,
   Inside the grounds
   'Round the Walls of Red Wing.

3. Oh, the gates are cast iron
   And the walls are barbed wire,
   Stay far from the fence
   With the 'lectricity sting
   And it's keep down your head
   And stay in your number,
   On the inside grounds
   'Round the Walls of Red Wing.

4. Oh, it's fare thee well
   To the deep hollow dungeon,
   Farewell to the boardwalk
   That takes you to the screen
   And farewell to the minutes
   They threaten you with it,
   Inside the grounds
   'Round the Walls of Red Wing.

5. It's many a guard
   That stands around smilin',
   Holdin' his club
   Like he was a king,
   Hopin' to get you
   Behind a wood pilin',
   Inside the grounds
   'Round the Walls of Red Wing.

6. The night aimed shadows
   Through the crossbar windows
   And the wind punched hard
   To make the wall siding sing,
   It's many a night
   I pretended to be a sleepin',
   On the inside grounds
   'Round the Walls of Red Wing.

7. As the rain rattled heavy
   On the bunk house shingles
   And the sounds in the night
   They made my ears ring,
   'Til the keys of the guards
   Clicked the tune of the morning,
   On the inside grounds
   'Round the Walls of Red Wing.

8. Oh, some of us'll end up
   In St. Cloud Prison
   And some of us'll
   Wind up to be lawyers and things,
   And some of us'll stand up to
   Meet you on your crossroads,
   From inside the grounds
   'Round the Walls of Red Wing.

With God on Our Side

WORDS AND MUSIC BY BOB DYLAN

Lyrics under the music:

there, _____ The laws to a - bide, _____ And that land that I

live in _____ Has God on its side. _____

2. Oh, the history books tell it,
   They tell it so well,
   The cavalries charged,
   The Indians fell.
   The cavalries charged,
   The Indians died,
   Oh the country was young
   With God on its side.

3. Oh, the Spanish American
   War had its day,
   And the Civil War too
   Was soon laid away,
   And the names of the heroes
   I's made to memorize,
   With guns in their hands
   And God on their side.

4. Oh, the first world war boys,
   It came and it went,
   The reason for fighting
   I never did get.
   But I learned to accept it,
   Accept it with pride,
   For you don't count the dead
   When God's on your side.

5. When the second world war
   Came to an end,
   We forgave the Germans
   And we were friends.
   Though they murdered six million
   In the ovens they fried,
   The Germans now too
   Have God on their side.

6. I've learned to hate Russians
   All through my whole life,
   If another war starts
   It's them we must fight.
   To hate them and fear them,
   To run and to hide,
   And accept it all bravely
   With God on my side.

7. But now we got weapons
   Of the chemical dust,
   If fire them we're forced to
   Then fire them we must.
   One push of the button
   And a shot the world wide,
   And you never ask questions
   When God's on your side.

8. In a many dark hour
   I've been thinkin' all this,
   That Jesus Christ
   Was betrayed by a kiss.
   But I can't think for you
   You'll have to decide,
   Whether Judas Iscariot
   Had God on his side.

9. So now as I'm leavin'
   I'm weary as Hell,
   The confusion I'm feelin'
   Ain't no time can tell.
   The words fill my head
   And fall to the floor,
   If God's on our side
   He'll stop the next war.

All I Really Want to Do

WORDS AND MUSIC BY BOB DYLAN

ny, _____ de-fy or cru-ci-fy you.

Refrain ALL I _____ REAL-LY _____ WANT TO DO _____ (falsetto)

Is Ba-by, be friends with you. _____

Verse 2:
No, and I ain't lookin' to fight with you,
Frighten you, or tighten you,
Drag you down, or bring you down,
Chain you down, or bring you down. (Refrain)

Verse 3:
I don't want to straight face you,
Race, or chase you, track or trace you,
Or disgrace you, or displace you,
Or define you, or confine you. (Refrain)

Verse 4:
I don't want to meet your kin,
Make you spin, or do you in,
Or select you, or dissect you,
Or inspect you, or reject you. (Refrain)

Verse 5:
I don't want to fake you out,
Take, or shake or forsake you out,
I ain't lookin' for you to feel like me,
See like me, or be like me. (Refrain)

Ballad in Plain D

WORDS AND MUSIC BY BOB DYLAN

2. Through young summer's breeze
    I stole her away
    From her mother and sister
    Though close did they stay,
    Each one of them suffering
    From the failures of their day,
    With strings of guilt
    They tried hard to guide us.

3. Of the two sisters
    I loved the young,
    With sensitive instincts
    She was the creative one,
    The constant scapegoat
    She was easily undone
    By the jealousy
    Of others around her.

4. For her parasite sister
    I had no respect
    Bound by her boredom
    Her pride to protect,
    Countless visions of the other
    She'd reflect
    As a crutch for her scenes
    And her society.

5. Myself, for what I did
    I cannot be excused,
    The changes I was going through
    Can't even be used.
    For the lies that I told her
    And hope not to lose
    The could-be dream lover
    Of my lifetime.

6. With unknown conciousness
    I possessed in my grip
    A magnificent mantelpiece,
    Though its heart being chipped,
    Noticing not
    That I'd already slipped
    To a sin
    Of love's false security.

7. From silhouetted anger
    To manufactured peace,
    Answers of emptiness
    Voice vacancies.
    Till the tombstones of damage
    Read me no questions but, "Please,
    What's wrong
    And what's exactly the matter?"

8. And so it did happen
    Like it could have been foreseen,
    The timeless explosion
    Of fantasy's dream.
    At the peak of the night
    The king and the queen
    Tumbled all down
    Into pieces.

9. The tragic figure!"
    Her sister did shout,
    "Leave her alone,
    God damn you, get out!"
    And I in my armor,
    Turning about
    And nailing her
    To the ruins of her pettiness.

10. Beneath a bare light bulb
    The plaster did pound
    Her sister and I
    In a screaming battleground,
    And she in between,
    The victim of sound,
    Soon shattered as a child
    'Neath her shadows.

11. All is gone, all is gone,
    Admit it, take flight,
    I gagged twice doubled
    Tears blinding my sight.
    My mind it was mangled,
    I ran into the night
    Leaving all of love's ashes
    Behind me.

12. The wind knock my window,
    The room it is wet,
    The words to say, "I'm sorry,"
    I haven't found yet.
    I think of her often
    And hope whoever she's met
    Will be fully aware
    Of how precious she is.

13. Ah, my friends,
    From the prison,
    They ask unto me,
    "How good, how good
    Does it feel to be free?"
    And I answer them most mysteriously,
    "Are birds free
    From the chains of the sky-way?"

It Ain't Me, Babe

WORDS AND MUSIC BY BOB DYLAN

1. Go 'way from my win - dow, ___ Leave at your own cho-sen speed, ___ I'm not the one you want, Babe, ___ I'm not the one you__ need. ___

2. Go lightly from the ledge Babe,
    Go lightly on the ground,
    I'm not the one you want, Babe,
    I will only let you down.
    You say you're looking for someone
    Who will promise never to part,
    Someone to close his eyes for you,
    Someone to close his heart.
    Someone who will die for you an' more
    But it ain't me, Babe,
    No, no, no it ain't me, Babe
    It ain't me you're looking for, Babe.

3. Go melt back into the nite Babe,
    Everything inside is made of stone,
    There's nothing in here moving
    An' anyway I'm not alone.
    You say you're looking for someone
    Who'll pick you up each time you fall,
    To gather flowers constantly
    An' to come each time you call.
    A lover for your life an' nothing more
    But it ain't me, Babe,
    No, no, no it ain't me, Babe,
    It ain't me you're looking for, Babe.

Black Crow Blues

WORDS AND MUSIC BY BOB DYLAN

Medium Blues tempo

1. I woke in the morn-in' wan-d'rin' Wast-ed and worn - out,__

I woke in the morn-in'wan-d'rin' Wast-ed and worn - out,__

Wish-in' my long lost lov-er__

2. I was standin' at the side road
   Listenin' to the billboard knock,
   Standin' at the side road
   Listenin' to the billboard knock,
   Well my wrist was empty
   But my nerves were kickin',
   Tickin' like a clock.

3. Here I got anything you need, Babe,
   Let me tell you in front,
   If I got anything you need, Babe,
   Let me tell you in front,
   You can come to me sometime,
   Night time, day time,
   Any time you want.

4. Sometimes I'm thinkin' I'm
   Too high to fall,
   Sometimes I'm thinkin' I'm
   Too high to fall,
   Other times I'm thinkin' I'm
   So low I don't know
   If I can come up at all.

5. Black crows in the meadow
   Across a broad highway,
   Black crows in the meadow
   Across a broad highway,
   Though it's funny, honey,
   I just don't feel much like a
   Scarecrow today.

Chimes of Freedom

WORDS AND MUSIC BY BOB DYLAN

1. Far be - tween sun-down's fin - ish an' mid-nite's bro - ken toll We ducked in - side the door - way thun - der crash-ing. As ma-jes-tic

bells   of   bolts _____ struck sha-dows   in   the   sounds _____

_____ Seem- ing   to   be   the   CHIMES   OF   FREE-DOM

flash- ing. _____ Flash-ing   for   the

war-ri- ors _____ whose strength   is   not   to   fight, _____

2. In the city's melted furnace, unexpectedly we watched
   With faces hidden while the walls were tightening,
   As the echo of the wedding bells before the blowin' rain
   Dissolved into the bells of the lightning.
   Tolling for the rebel, tolling for the rake,
   Tolling for the luckless, the abandoned an' forsaked,
   Tolling for the outcast, burnin' constantly at stake
   An' we gazed upon the chimes of freedom flashing.

3. Thru the mad mystic hammering of the wild ripping hail
   The sky cracked its poems in naked wonder
   That the clinging of the church bells blew far into the breeze
   Leaving only bells of lightning and its thunder
   Striking for the gentle, striking for the kind,
   Striking for the guardians and protectors of the mind
   An' the unpawned painter behind beyond his rightful time
   An' we gazed upon the chimes of freedom flashing.

4. Thru the wild cathedral evening the rain unraveled tales
   For the disrobed faceless forms of no position
   Tolling for the tongues with no place to bring their thoughts
   All down in taken for granted situations
   Tolling for the deaf an' blind, tolling for the mute,
   Tolling for the mistreated, mateless mother, the mistitled prostitute,
   For the misdemeanor outlaw chased an' cheated by pursuit
   An' we gazed upon the chimes of freedom flashing.

5. Even tho a cloud's white curtain in a far off corner flashed
   An' the hypnotic splattered mist was slowly lifting
   Electric light still struck like arrows fired but for the ones
   Condemned to drift or else be kept from drifting
   Tolling for the searching ones, on their speechless seeking trail
   For the lonesome hearted lovers, with too personal a tale
   An' for each unharmful gentle soul misplaced inside a jail
   An' we gazed upon the chimes of freedom flashing.

6. Starry eyed an' laughing as I recall when we were caught
   Trapped by no track of hours for they hanged suspended
   As we listened one last time an' we watched with one last look
   Spellbound an' swallowed till the tolling ended
   Tolling for the aching ones whose wounds cannot be nursed
   For the countless confused, accused, misused, stung out ones an' worse
   An' for every hung up person in the whole wide universe
   An' we gazed upon the chimes of freedom flashing.

I Don't Believe You

WORDS AND MUSIC BY BOB DYLAN

Medium bright

1. I can't un-der-stand, She let go of my hand An' left me here fac-ing the

wall. _____ I'd sure like t' know Why she did go But

I can't get close t'her at all. _____ Though we kissed thru the wild blaz-ing

night - time_ She said she would nev-er for - get_ But now_ morn-in's clear, It's

like I ain't here, She just acts like we nev-er have met. _____

D.S. 4 times

2. It's all new t' me
   Like some mystery
   It could even be like a myth
   Yet it's hard t' think on
   That she's the same one
   That last night I was with.
   From darkness, dreams 're deserted
   Am I still dreamin' yet?
   I wish she'd unlock
   Her voice once an' talk
   'Stead of actin' like we never have met.

3. If she ain't feelin' well
   Then why don't she tell
   'Stead of turnin' her back t' my face?
   Without any doubt
   She seems too far out
   For me t' return t' her chase.
   Though the night ran swirling an' whirling
   I remember her whispering yet.
   But evidently she don't
   An' evidently she won't,
   She just acts like we never have met.

4. If I didn't have t' guess
   I'd gladly confess
   T' anything I might've tried.
   If I was with 'er too long
   Or have done something wrong
   I wish she'd tell me what it is, I'll run an' hide
   Tho her skirt it swayed as a guitar played
   Her mouth was watery and wet
   But now something has changed
   For she ain't the same
   She just acts like we never have met.

5. I'm leavin' today
   I'll be on my way
   Of this I can't say very much
   But if you want me to
   I can be just like you
   An' pretend that we never have touched
   An' if anybody asks me, "Is it easy to forget?"
   I'll say, "It's easily done,
   You just pick anyone,
   An' pretend that you never have met!"

Motorpsycho Nightmare

WORDS AND MUSIC BY BOB DYLAN

1. I pound-ed on a farm-house look-in' for a place to stay, I was might-y, might-y tired___ I had gone a long, long way,___ I said, "Hey, hey, in there, is there

an - y - bod - y home?" I was stand - in' on the

steps feel - in' most a - lone.___ Well, out comes a

farm - er, he must have thought that I was nuts, He im -

me-di-ate-ly looked at me, and stuck a gun in-to my guts.

D.S.
8 *times*

2. I fell down
   To my bended knees
   Saying, "I dig farmers,
   Don't shoot, please!"
   He cocked his rifle
   And began to shout,
   "You're that travelin' salesman
   That I have heard about.
   I said, "No! No! No!
   I'm a doctor and it's true
   I'm a clean cut kid
   And I been to college, too. "

3. Then in comes his daughter
   Whose name was Rita
   She looked like she stepped out of
   A "Dolce Vita. "
   I immediately tried to cool it
   With her dad
   And told him what a
   Nice, pretty farm he had.
   He said, "What do doctors
   Know about farms, pray tell?"
   I said, "I was born
   At the bottom of a wishing well. "

4. Well, by the dirt 'neath my nails
   I guess he knew I wouldn't lie
   "I guess you're tired, "
   He said, kinda sly.
   I said, "Yes, ten thousand miles
   Today, I drove. "
   He said, "I got a bed for you
   Underneath the stove,
   Just one condition
   And you go to sleep right now.
   That you don't touch my daughter
   And in the morning, milk the cow. "

5. I was sleepin' like a rat
   When I heard something jerkin'
   There stood Rita
   Lookin' just like Tony Perkins.
   She said, "Would you like to take a shower?
   I'll show you up to the door. "
   I said, "Oh, no! no!
   I've been through this before. "
   I knew I had to split
   But I didn't know how
   When she said,
   "Would you like to take that shower, now?"

6. Well, I couldn't leave
   Unless the old man chased me out
   Cause I'd already promised
   That I'd milk his cows.
   I had to say something
   To strike him very weird,
   So I yelled out
   "I like Fidel Castro and his beard. "
   Rita looked offended
   But she got out of the way
   As he came charging down the stairs
   Sayin', "What's that I heard you say?"

7. I said, "I like Fidel Castro,
   I think you heard me right, "
   And ducked as he swung
   At me with all his might
   Rita mumbled something,
   'Bout her mother on the hill,
   As his fist hit the icebox,
   He said he's going to kill me
   If I don't get out the door
   In two seconds flat
   You unpatriotic
   Rotten doctor, Commie rat.

8. Well, he threw a Reader's Digest
   At my head and I did run,
   I did a somersault
   As I seen him get his gun.
   And crashed through the window
   At a hundred miles an hour
   And landed fully blast
   In his garden flowers.
   Rita said, "Come back!"
   As he started to load
   The sun was comin' up
   And I was runnin' down the road.

9. Well, I don't figure I'll be back
   There for a spell,
   Even though Rita moved away
   And got a job in a motel
   He still waits for me
   Constant, on the sly,
   He wants to turn me in
   To the F.B.I.
   Me, I romp and stomp
   Thankful as I romp,
   Without freedom of speech
   I might be in the swamp.

To Ramona

WORDS AND MUSIC BY BOB DYLAN

1. Ra - mo - na, come clos - er, Shut soft - ly your wa - ter - y eyes,

The pangs of your sad - ness Shall pass as your sens - es will rise,

62

2. Your cracked country lips
    I still wish to kiss
    As to be under the strength of your skin,
    Your magnetic movements
    Still capture the minutes I'm in,
    But it grieves my heart, love,
    To see you tryin' to be a part of
    A world that just don't exist;
    It's all just a dream, Babe,
    A vacuum, a scheme, Babe,
    That sucks you into feelin' like this.

3. I can see that your head
    Has been twisted and fed
    By worthless foam from the mouth,
    I can tell you are torn
    Between stayin' and returnin'
    On back to the south,
    You've been fooled into thinking
    That the finishin' end is at hand,
    Yet there's no one to beat you,
    No one t' defeat you,
    'Cept the thoughts of yourself feeling bad.

4. I've heard you say many times
    That you're better'n no one
    An' no one is better'n you,
    If you really believe that,
    You know you got
    Nothin' to win, and nothin' to lose,
    From fixtures an' forces an' friends
    Your sorrow does stem,
    That hype you and type you,
    Makin' you feel
    That you must be exactly like them.

5. I'd forever talk to you
    But soon my words,
    They would turn into a meaningless ring,
    For deep in my heart
    I know there is no help I can bring,
    Everything passes
    Everything changes,
    Just do what you think you should do,
    As someday maybe,
    Who knows, Baby,
    I'll come and be cryin' to you.

Spanish Harlem Incident

WORDS AND MUSIC BY BOB DYLAN

Moderato

1. Gyp-sy gal — the hands of Har-lem Can-not hold — you to its heat — Your tem-p'ra-ture's — too hot for tam-ing, Your flam-ing feet — burn up the street. I am home-less

2. Gypsy gal, you got me swallowed,
   I have fallen far beneath
   Your pearly eyes so fast an' slashing,
   An' your flashing diamond teeth.
   The night is pitch black, come an' make my
   Pale face fit into place (Ah, please!)
   Let me know, Babe I got to know, Babe,
   If it's you my life-lines trace.

3. I been wond'rin' all about me
   Ever since I seen you there
   On the cliffs of your wildcat charms I'm riding.
   I know I'm 'round you but I don't know where.
   You have slayed me, you have made me,
   I got to laugh half-ways off my heels
   I got to know, Babe, will I be touching you
   So I can tell if I'm really real?

Bob Dylan's Dream

WORDS AND MUSIC BY BOB DYLAN

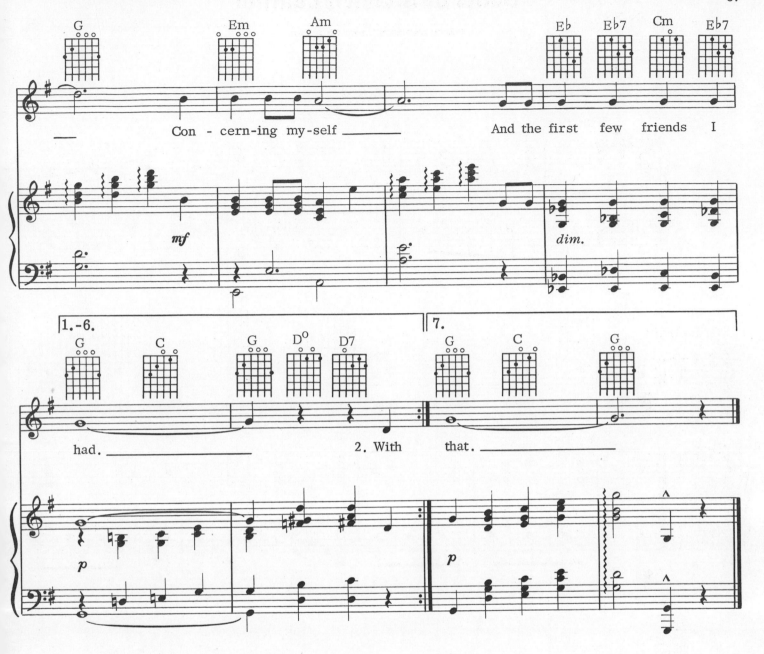

2. With half damp eyes I stared to the room
   Where my friends and I spent many an afternoon,
   Where we together weathered many a storm,
   Laughin' and singin' till the early hours of
      the morn.

3. By the old wooden stove where our hats was hung,
   Our words were told our songs were sung;
   Where we longed for nothin' and were quite satisfied
   Talkin' and a-jokin' about the wicked world outside.

4. With haunted hearts through the heat and cold,
   We never thought we could ever get old;
   We thought we could sit forever in fun
   But our chances really was a million to one.

5. As easy it was to tell black from white,
   It was all that easy to tell wrong from right;
   And our choices were few and the thought never hit
   That the one road we traveled would ever
      shatter and split.

6. How many a year has passed and gone,
   And many a gamble has been lost and won;
   And many a road taken by many a friend,
   And each one I've never seen again.

7. I wish, I wish, I wish in vain,
   That we could sit simply in that room again;
   Ten thousand dollars at the drop of a hat,
   I'd give it all gladly if our lives could be like that.

Boots of Spanish Leather

WORDS AND MUSIC BY BOB DYLAN

1. Oh I'm sail - in' a - way my own true love, I'm sail - in' a -
way in the morn - ing. _____ Is there some - thing I can send you from a -

cross   the   sea,   From the place   that   I'll   be   land - ing?_____

2. No there's nothin' you can send me my own true love,
   There's nothin' I wish to be ownin',
   Just carry yourself back to me unspoiled,
   From across that lonesome ocean.

3. Oh, but I just thought you might long want something fine
   Made of silver or of golden,
   Either from the mountains of Madrid
   Or from the coast of Barcelona.

4. Oh but if I had the stars from the darkest night
   And the diamonds from the deepest ocean,
   I'd forsake them all for your sweet kiss
   For that's all I'm wishin' to be ownin'.

5. That I might be gone a long ole time
   And it's only that I'm askin',
   Is there somethin' I can send you to remember me by
   To make your time more easy passin'.

6. Oh how can, how can you ask me again,
   It only brings me sorrow,
   The same thing I want from you today
   I would want again tomorrow.

7. I got a letter on a lonesome day,
   It was from her ship a-sailin'
   Saying I don't know when I'll be comin' back again,
   It depends on how I'm a-feelin'.

8. Well, if you my love must think that-a-way,
   I'm sure your mind is roamin',
   I'm sure your heart is not with me,
   But with the country to where you're goin'.

9. So take heed, take heed of the western wind,
   Take heed of the stormy weather,
   And yes, there's something you can send back to me,
   Spanish boots of Spanish leather.

Don't Think Twice, It's All Right

WORDS AND MUSIC BY BOB DYLAN

Eternal Circle

WORDS AND MUSIC BY BOB DYLAN

C

spun, _____ She called with her eyes, To the

E7

F **C**

tune I's a - play-in', _____ But the song it was

C **Am6** **Fm** **G7** **C**

Repeat 4 times

long _ And I'd on - ly be - gun. _____

2. Oh a bullet of light
   Her face was reflectin',
   The fast fading words
   That rolled from my tongue.

   With a long distance look
   Her eyes was on fire,
   But the song it was long
   And there was more to be sung.

4. I glanced at my guitar
   And played it pretendin'
   That of all the eyes out there
   I could see none.

   As the thoughts pounded hard
   Like the pierce of an arrow,
   But the song it was long
   And it had to get done.

3. My eyes danced a circle
   Across her clear outline,
   With her head tilted sideways
   She called me again.

   As the tune drifted out
   She breathed hard to the echo,
   But the song it was long
   And it was far to the end.

5. As the tune finally folded
   I laid down the guitar,
   Then looked for the girl
   Who'd stayed for so long.

   But her shadow was missin'
   For all of my searchin',
   So I picked up my guitar
   And began the next song.

Farewell

WORDS AND MUSIC BY BOB DYLAN

meet an-oth-er day, an-oth-er time, _____ It ain't the leav-in' That's a-
griev - in' me But my {true love} who's bound to stay be - hind.
But my {dar - lin'}

Repeat 4 times

2. Oh the weather is against me and the wind blows hard
   And the rain she's a-turnin' into hail,
   I still might strike it lucky on a highway goin' west
   Though I'm travelin' on a path beaten trail.

   REFRAIN:

3. I will write you a letter from time to time,
   As I'm ramblin' you can travel with me too.
   With my head, my heart, and my hands, my love,
   I will send what I learn back home to you.

   REFRAIN:

4. I will tell you of the laughter and of troubles,
   Be them somebody else's or my own;
   With my hands in my pockets and my coat collar high
   I will travel unnoticed and unknown.

   REFRAIN:

5. I've heard tell of a town where I might as well be bound,
   It's down around the old Mexican plains,
   They say that the people are all friendly there
   And all they ask of you is your name.

   REFRAIN:

North Country Blues

WORDS AND MUSIC BY BOB DYLAN

card-board filled win-dows, And old men on the bench-es, Tell you now that the whole town is emp-ty.

Repeat 9 times

2. In the north end of town,
   My own children are grown
   But I was raised on the other.
   In the wee hours of youth,
   My mother took sick,
   And I was brought up by my brother.

3. The iron ore poured
   As the years passed the door,
   The drag lines an' the shovels they was a-humming.
   'Til one day my brother
   Failed to come home,
   The same as my father before him.

4. Well a long winter's wait
   From the window I watched,
   My friends they couldn't have been kinder.
   And my school it was cut
   As I quit in the spring,
   To marry John Thomas, a miner.

5. Oh the years passed again
   And the givin' was good,
   With the lunch bucket filled every season.
   What with three babies born,
   The work was cut down,
   To a half a day's shift with no reason.

6. Then the shaft was soon shut,
   And my work was cut,
   And the firing air it felt frozen.
   'Til a man come to speak
   And he said in one week
   That number eleven was closin'.

7. They complained in the East
   They are paying too high,
   They say that your ore ain't worth digging.
   That it's much cheaper down
   In the South American town,
   Where the miners work almost for nothing.

8. So the mining gates locked
   And the red iron rotted
   And the room smelled heavy from drinking.
   Where the sad, silent song
   Made the hour twice as long
   As I waited for the sun to go sinking.

9. I lived by the window
   As he talked to himself,
   This silence of tongues it was building.
   Then one morning's week,
   The bed it was bare,
   And I's left alone with three children.

10. The summer is gone,
    The ground's turning cold,
    The stars one by one they're a-foldin'.
    My children will go
    As soon as they grow,
    Well, there ain't nothing here now to hold them.

Only a Pawn in Their Game

WORDS AND MUSIC BY BOB DYLAN

D.S. 4 times

on - ly   a   pawn   in   their   game. _____

last time fade

2. A south politician preaches to the poor, white man,
   You got more than the blacks, don't complain,
   You're better than them, you been born with white skin, they explain,
   And the negro is named,
      *Is used it is plain,
      For the politician's gain,
      As he rises to fame,
      And the poor white remains,
      On the caboose of the train,
      But it ain't him to blame,
   He's only a pawn in their game.

3. The deputy sheriffs, the soldiers, the governors get paid,
   And the marshals and cops get the same,
   But the poor white man's used in the hands of them all like a tool,
   He's taught in his school
      *From the start by the rule
      That the laws are with him
      To protect his white skin,
      To keep up his hate
      So he never thinks straight,
      'Bout the shape that he's in,
      But it ain't him to blame,
   He's only a pawn in their game.

4. From the poverty shacks he looks from the cracks to the tracks,
   And the hoof beats pound in his brain,
   And he's taught how to walk in a pack,
   Shoot in the back,
      *With his fist in a clinch,
      To hang and to lynch,
      To hide 'neath the hood,
      To kill with no pain
      Like a dog on a chain,
      He ain't got no name
      But it ain't him to blame,
   He's only a pawn in their game.

5. The day Medgar Evers was buried from the bullet he caught,
   They lowered him down as a king,
   But when the shadowy sun sets on the one
   That fired the gun,
      *He'll see by his grave
      On the stone that remains,
      Carved next to his name
      His epitaph plain,
   Only a pawn in their game.

Paths of Victory

WORDS AND MUSIC BY BOB DYLAN

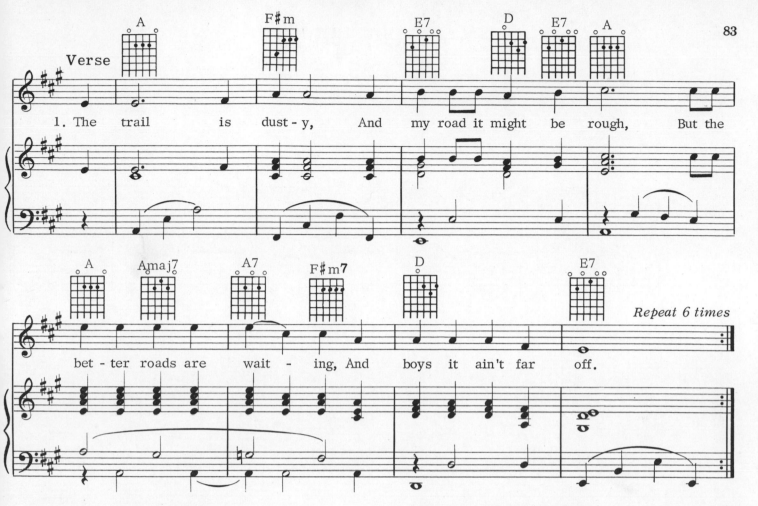

Verse

1. The trail is dust-y, And my road it might be rough, But the
bet-ter roads are wait-ing, And boys it ain't far off.

Repeat 6 times

REFRAIN 2. Trails of troubles,
Roads of battles,
Paths of victory,
We shall walk.

VERSE 2. I walked down by the river,
I turned my head up high,
I saw that silver linin'
That was hangin' in the sky.

REFRAIN 4. Trails of troubles,
Roads of battles,
Paths of victory,
We shall walk.

VERSE 4. The gravel road is bumpy,
It's a hard road to ride,
But there's a clearer road a-waitin'
With the cinders on the side.

REFRAIN 3. Trails of troubles,
Roads of battles,
Paths of victory,
We shall walk.

VERSE 3. The evenin' dusk was rollin',
I was walking down the track,
There was a one-way wind a-blowin'
And it was blowin' at my back.

REFRAIN 5. Trails of troubles,
Roads of battles,
Paths of victory,
We shall walk.

VERSE 5. That evening train was rollin',
The hummin' of its wheels,
My eyes they saw a better day
As I looked across the fields.

REFRAIN 6. Trails of troubles,
Roads of battles,
Paths of victory,
We shall walk.

VERSE 6. The trail is dusty,
The road it might be rough,
But the good road is a-waitin'
And boys it ain't far off.

REFRAIN 7. Trails of troubles,
Roads of battles,
Paths of victory,
We shall walk.

Seven Curses

WORDS AND MUSIC BY BOB DYLAN

2. Old Reilly's daughter got a message
   That her father was goin' to hang
   She rode by night and came by morning
   With gold and silver in her hand.

3. When the judge he saw Reilly's daughter
   His old eyes deepened in his head
   Sayin' gold will never free your father
   The price, my dear, is you instead.

4. Oh, I'm as good as dead cried Reilly,
   It's only you that he does crave
   And my skin will surely crawl if he
           touches you at all,
   Get on your horse and ride away.

5. Oh father you will surely die
   If I don't take the chance to try
   And pay the price and not take your advice
   For that reason I will have to stay.

6. The gallows shadows shook the evening,
   In the night a hound dog bayed,
   In the night the grounds were groanin',
   In the night the price was paid.

7. The next mornin' she had awoken
   To know that the judge had never spoken,
   She saw that hangin' branch a-bendin'
   She saw her father's body broken.

8. These be seven curses on a judge so cruel
   That one doctor will not save him
   That two healers will not heal him
   That three eyes will not see him.

9. That four ears will not hear him
   That five walls will not hide him
   That six diggers will not bury him
   And that seven deaths shall never kill him.

When the Ship Comes In

WORDS AND MUSIC BY BOB DYLAN

1. Oh the time will come up When the winds will stop And the breeze will cease to be breath-in' _____ Like the still-ness in the wind 'Fore the hur-ri-cane be-gins The ho-ur WHEN THE SHIP COMES IN. Oh the seas will split And the ship will hit And the

shore-line sands will be shak-ing___ Then the tide will sound And the wind will pound And the

D.S. 3 times %

morn-ing will be break - ing. ___

2. Oh the fishes will laugh
   As they swim out of the path
   And the seagulls they'll be smiling
   And the rocks on the sand
   Will proudly stand
   The hour that the ship comes in.

   And the words they use
   For to get the ship confused
   Will not be understood as they're spoken
   For the chains of the sea
   Will have busted in the night
   And will be buried at the bottom of the ocean.

3. A song will lift
   As the mainsail shifts
   And the boat drifts on to the shore line
   And the sun will respect
   Every face on the deck
   The hour when the ship comes in.

   Then the sands will roll
   Out a carpet of gold
   For your weary toes to be a touchin'
   And the ship's wise men
   Will remind you once again
   That the whole wide world is watchin'.

4. Oh the foes will rise
   With the sleep still in their eyes
   And they'll jerk from their beds and think they're dreamin'
   But they'll pinch themselves and squeal
   And know that it's for real
   The hour when the ship comes in.

   Then they'll raise their hands
   Sayin' we'll meet all your demands
   But we'll shout from the bow your days are numbered
   And like Pharoah's triumph
   They'll be drownded in the tide
   And like Goliath they'll be conquered.

Bob Dylan's 115th Dream

WORDS AND MUSIC BY BOB DYLAN

* Pronounced AY-RAB

2. I think I'll call it America
    I said as we hit land
    I took a deep breath
    I fell down, I could not stand
    Captain* Arab he started
    Writing up some deeds
    He said, let's set up a fort
    And start buying the place with beads
    Just then this cop comes down the street
    Crazy as a loon
    He throws us all in jail
    For carryin' harpoons.

3. Ah me I busted out
    Don't even ask me how
    I went to get some help
    I walked by a guernsey cow
    Who directed me down
    To the Bowery slums
    Where people carried signs around
    Sayin', ban the bums
    I jumped right into line
    Sayin', I hope that I'm not late
    When I realized I hadn't eaten
    For five days straight.

4. I went to a restaurant
    Lookin' for the cook
    I told them I was the editor
    Of a famous etiquette book
    The waitress he was handsome
    He wore a powder blue cape
    I ordered some suzette, I said
    Could you please make that crepe'
    Just then the whole kitchen exploded
    From bolin' fat
    Food was flyin' everywhere
    And I left without my hat.

5. Now I didn't mean to be nosey
    But I went into a bank
    To get some bail for Arab*
    And all the boys back in the tank
    They asked me for some collateral
    And I pulled down my pants
    They threw me in the alley
    When up comes this girl from France
    Who invited me to her house
    I went, but she had a friend
    Who knocked me out
    And robbed my boots
    And I was on the street again.

6. Well I rapped upon a house
    With the U. S. flag upon display
    I said, could you help me out
    I got some friends down the way
    The man says, get out of here
    I'll tear you limb from limb
    I said, you know they refused Jesus too
    He said, you're not him
    Get out of here before I break your bones
    I ain't your pop
    I decided to have him arrested
    And I went lookin' for a cop.

7. I ran right outside
    And I hopped inside a cab
    I went out the other door
    This Englishman said, fab
    As he saw me leap a hot dog stand
    And a chariot that stood
    Parked across from a building
    Advertising brotherhood
    I ran right through the front door
    Like a hobo sailor does
    But it was just a funeral parlor
    And the man asked me who I was.

8. I repeated that my friends
    Were all in jail, with a sigh
    He gave me his card
    He said, call me if they die
    I shook his hand and said goodby
    Ran out to the street
    When a bowling ball came down the road
    And knocked me off my feet
    A pay phone was ringin'
    It just about blew my mind
    When I picked it up and said hello
    This foot came through the line.

9. Well by this time I was fed up
    At tryin' to make a stab
    At bringin' back any help
    For my friends and captain Arab*
    I decided to flip a coin
    Like either heads or tails
    Would let me know if I should go
    Back to ship or back to jail
    So I hocked my sailors suit
    And I got a coin to flip
    It came up tails
    It rhymed my sails
    So I made it back to the ship.

10. Well I got back and took
    The parkin' ticket off the mast
    I was ripping it to shreds
    When this coastguard boat went past
    They asked me my name
    And I said, Captain Kidd
    They believed me but
    They wanted to know
    What exactly that I did
    I said for the Pope of Eruke
    I was employed
    They let me go right away
    They were very paranoid.

11. Well, the last I heard of Arab*
    He was stuck on a whale
    That was married to the deputy
    Sheriff of the jail
    But the funniest thing was
    When I was leavin' the bay
    I saw three ships a sailin'
    They were all heading my way
    I asked the captain what his name was
    And how come he didn't drive a truck
    He said his name was Columbus
    I just said, good luck.

Maggie's Farm

WORDS AND MUSIC BY BOB DYLAN

1. I ain't gon - na work on MAG - GIE'S FARM no more ___

No, I ain't gon - na work on MAG - GIE'S

2. I ain't gonna work for Maggie's brother no more
No, I ain't gonna work for Maggie's brother no more
Well he hands you a nickel
He hands you a dime
He asks with a grin
If you're havin' a good time
Then he fines you every time you slam the door
I ain't gonna work for Maggie's brother no more.

3. I ain't gonna work for Maggie's pa no more
No, I ain't gonna work for Maggie's pa no more
Well he puts his cigar
Out in your face just for kicks
His bedroom window
It is made out of bricks
The National Guard stands around his door
Ah, I ain't gonna work for Maggie's pa no more.

4. I ain't gonna work for Maggie's ma no more
No, I ain't gonna work for Maggie's ma no more
Well she talks to all the servants
About man and God and law
Everybody says she's the brains behind pa
She's sixty-eight, but she says she's twenty-four
I ain't gonna work for Maggie's ma no more.

5. I ain't gonna work on Maggie's farm no more
I ain't gonna work on Maggie's farm no more
Well, I try my best
To be just like I am
But everybody wants you
To be just like them
They sing while you slave
And I just get bored
I ain't gonna work on Maggie's farm no more.

The Gates of Eden

WORDS AND MUSIC BY BOB DYLAN

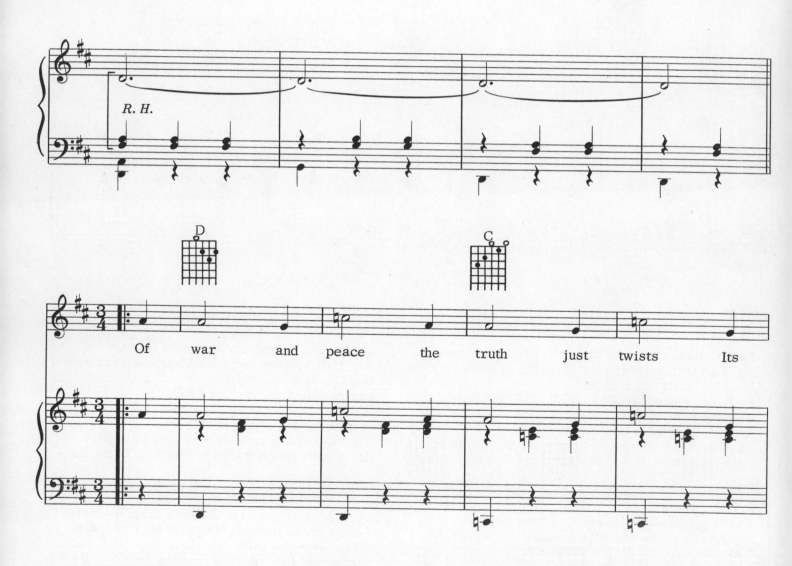

Of war and peace the truth just twists Its

2. The lamp post stands with folded arms
   Its iron claws attached
   To curbs 'neath holes where babies wail
   Though it shadows metal badge
   All in all can only fall
   With a crashing but meaningless blow
   No sound ever comes from The Gates of Eden.

3. This savage soldier sticks his head in sand
   And then complains
   Unto the shoeless hunter who's gone deaf
   But still remains
   Upon the beach where hound dogs bay
   At ships with tattoed sails
   Heading for The Gates of Eden.

4. With a time rusted compass blade
   Aladdin and his lamp
   Sits with Utopian hermit monks
   Side saddle on the Golden Calf
   And on their promises of paradise
   You will not hear a laugh
   All except inside The Gates of Eden.

5. Relationships of ownership
   They whisper in the wings
   To those condemned to act accordingly
   And wait for succeeding kings
   And I try to harmonize with songs
   The lonesome sparrow sings
   There are no kings inside The Gates of Eden.

6. The motorcycle black madonna
   Two wheeled gypsy queen
   And her silver studded phantom cause
   The grey flannel dwarf to scream
   As he weeps to wicked birds of prey
   Who pick up on his bread crumb sins
   And there are no sins inside The Gades of Eden.

7. The Kingdoms of experience
   In the precious winds they rot
   While paupers change possessions
   Each one wishing for what the other has got
   And the princess and the prince
   Discuss what's real and what is not
   It doesn't matter inside The Gates of Eden.

8. The foreign sun it squints upon
   A bed that is never mine
   As friends and other strangers
   From their fates try to resign
   Leaving men holy totally free
   To do anything they wish to do but die
   And there are no trials inside The Gates of Eden.

9. At dawn my lover comes to me
   And tells me of her dreams
   With no attempts to shovel the glimpse
   Into the ditch of what each one means
   At times I think there are no words
   But these to tell what's true
   And there are no truths outside The Gates of Eden.

It's All Over Now, Baby Blue

WORDS AND MUSIC BY BOB DYLAN

Cry-ing like a fire_ in the sun._____ Look out the_

Saints are com- in' through _____ And IT'S ALL O - VER

NOW, BA - BY BLUE. _

2. The highway is for gamblers, better use your sins
Take what you have gathered from coincidence
The empty handed painter from your streets
Is drawing crazy patterns on your sheets
This sky too, is folding under you
And it's all over now, baby blue.

3. All your seasick sailors, they are rowing home
All your reindeer armies, are all going home
The lover who just walked out your door
Has taken all his blankets from the floor
The carpet too, is moving under you
And it's all over now, baby blue.

4. Leave your stepping stones behind, something calls for you
Forget the dead you've left, they will not follow you
The vagabond who's rapping at your door
Is standing in the clothes that you once wore
Strike another match, go start anew
And it's all over now, baby blue.

It's Alright Ma (I'm Only Bleeding)

WORDS AND MUSIC BY BOB DYLAN

un-der-stand you know too soon, There is no sense in try-ing.

Point-ed threats they bluff with scorn Su-i-cide re-marks are torn From the fool's gold

mouth-piece The hol-low horn plays wast-ed words Proved to warn That

he not bus-y be-ing born _____ Is bus-y dy-ing.

* The asterisks denote ad lib guitar breaks which occur at these points in the Dylan recording.

ear IT'S AL - RIGHT MA, _____ I'm on - ly sigh-ing.

2. As some warn victory, some downfall
   Private reasons great or small
   Can be seen in the eyes of those that call
   To make all that should be killed, to crawl
   While others say, don't hate nothin' at all
   Except hatred

   Disillusioned words like bullets bark
   As human Gods aim for their mark
   Made everything from toy guns that spark
   To flesh colored Christs that glow in the dark
   It's easy to see without lookin' too far
   That not much,
   Is really sacred

   While preachers preach of evil fates
   Teachers teach that knowledge waits
   Can lead to hundred dollar plates
   Goodness hides behind its gates
   But even the president of the United States
   Sometimes must have
   To stand naked
   And though the rules of the road, have been lodged
   It's only peoples games that you got to dodge
   And it's alright ma, I can make it.

3. Advertising signs that con you
   Into thinking you're the one
   That can do what's never been done
   That can win, what's never been won
   Meantime life outside goes on
   All around you

   You lose yourself, you reappear
   You suddenly find you got nothin' to fear
   Alone you stand, with nobody near
   When a trembling distant voice unclear
   Startles your sleeping ears to hear
   That somebody thinks
   They really found you

   A question in your nerves is lit
   Yet you know there is no answer fit to satisfy.
   Insure you not to quit
   To keep it in your mind and not fergit
   That it is not he or she or them or it
   That you belong to
   Although the masters make the rules
   Of the wise men and the fools
   I got nothing, ma
   To live up to.

* 4. For them that must obey authority
     That they do not respect in any degree
     Who despise their jobs, their destinies
     Speak jealously of them that are free
     Cultivate their flowers to be
     Nothing more than something
     They invest in

     While some unprinciples baptized
     To strict party platform ties
     Social clubs in drag disguise
     Outsiders achin' freely criticize
     Tell nothin' except who to idolize
     And say God bless him

     While one who sings with his tongue on fire
     Gargles in the rat race choir
     Bent out of shape from society's pliers
     Cares not to come up any higher
     But rather get you down in the hole
     That he's in
     But I mean no harm, nor put fault
     On anyone that lives in a vault
     But it's alright ma, if I can please him

*5. Old lady judges watch people in pairs
    Limited in sex, they dare
    To push fake moral insult, and stare
    While money doesn't talk, it swears
    Obscenity, who really cares
    Propaganda, all is phony

    While them that defend what they cannot see
    With a killer's pride, security
    It blows the minds most bitterly
    For them that think death's honesty
    Won't fall upon them naturally
    Life sometimes
    Must get lonely

    My eyes collide head on with stuffed graveyards,
    False Gods, I scuff
    At pettiness which plays so rough
    Walk upside down inside handcuffs
    Kick my legs to crash it off
    Say okay, I've had enough
    What else can you show me
    And if my thought dreams could be seen
    They'd probably put my head in a guillotine
    But it's alright ma
    It's life, and life only.

Love Minus Zero/No Limit

WORDS AND MUSIC BY BOB DYLAN

Peo - ple car - ry ros - es   And make prom-is-es by the hours ___

My love she laughs like the flow-ers ___ Val - en-tines can't buy her. ___

Repeat 3 times

2. In the dime stores and bus stations
People talk of situations
Read books, repeat quotations
Draw conclusions on the wall
Some speak of the future
My love, she speaks softly
She knows there's no success like failure
And that failure's no success at all.

3. The cloak and dagger dangles
Madams light the candles
In ceremonies of the horsemen
Even the pawn must hold a grudge
Statues made of match sticks
Crumble into one another
My love winks, she does not bother
She knows too much to argue or to judge.

4. The bridge at midnight trembles
The country doctor rambles
Bankers' nieces seek perfection
Expecting all the gifts that wise men bring
The wind howls like a hammer
The night blows cold an' rainy
My love she's like some raven
At my window with a broken wing.

Mr. Tambourine Man

WORDS AND MUSIC BY BOB DYLAN

5th time Fine

jin-gle jan-gle morn-in' I'll come fol-low-in' you.

Verse

1. Though I know that eve-nin's em-pire has re-turned in-to sand,

Van-ished from my hand, Left me blind-ly here to stand but still not

sleep-in'! My wea-ri-ness a-maz-es me I'm

brand-ed on my feet. I have no one to meet And the

an-cient emp-ty street's too dead for dream-in'. _____

Repeat 3 times

Refrain:

Verse 2. Take me on a trip upon your magic swirlin' ship
My senses have been stripped, my hands can't feel to grip
My toes too numb to step, wait only for my boot heels
To be wanderin'
I'm ready to go anywhere, I'm ready for to fade
Into my own parade, cast your dancin' spell my way
I promise to go under it.

Refrain:

Verse 3. Though you might hear laughin' spinnin' swingin' madly across the sun
It's not aimed at anyone, it's just escapin' on the run
And but for the sky there are no fences facin'
And if you hear vague traces of skippin' reels of rhyme
To your tambourine in time, it's just a ragged clown behind
I wouldn't pay it any mind, it's just a shadow you're
Seein' that he's chasin'.

Refrain:

Verse 4. Then take me disappearin' through the smoke rings of my mind
Down the foggy ruins of time, far past the frozen leaves
The haunted, frightened trees out to the windy beach
Far from the twisted reach of crazy sorrow
Yes, to dance beneath the diamond sky with one hand wavin' free
Silhouetted by the sea, circled by the circus sands
With all memory and fate driven deep beneath the waves
Let me forget about today until tomorrow.

Refrain:

Subterranean Homesick Blues

WORDS AND MUSIC BY BOB DYLAN

cap By the big pen Wants e-lev-en dol-lar bills You on-ly got ten.

Interlude

Repeat 3 times

2. Maggie comes fleet foot
   Face full of black soot
   Talkin' at the heat put
   Plants in the bed but
   The phone's tapped any way
   Maggie says that many say
   They must bust in early May
   Orders from the D. A.
   Look out kid
   Don't matter what you did
   Walk on your tip toes
   Don't try "No Doz"
   Better stay away from those
   That carry around a fire hose
   Keep a clean nose
   Watch the plain clothes
   You don't need a weather man
   To know which way the wind blows.

3. Get sick, get well
   Hang around a ink well
   Ring bell, hard to tell
   Of anything is goin' to sell
   Try hard, get barred
   Get back, write braille
   Get jailed, jump bail
   Join the army, if you fail
   Look out kid, you're gonna get hit
   But users, cheaters
   Six time losers
   Hang around the theatres
   Girl by the whirlpool
   Lookin' for a new fool
   Don't follow leaders
   Watch the parkin' meters

4. Ah get born, keep warm
   Short pants, romance, learn to dance
   Get dressed, get blessed
   Try to be a success
   Please her, please him, buy gifts
   Don't steal, don't lift
   Twenty years of schoolin'
   And they put you on the day shift
   Look out kid they keep it all hid
   Better jump down a manhole
   Light yourself a candle, don't wear sandals
   Try to avoid the scandals
   Don't wanna be a bum
   You better chew gum
   The pump don't work
   'cause the vandals took the handles.

On the Road Again

WORDS AND MUSIC BY BOB DYLAN

2. Well I go to pet your monkey
   I get a face full of claws
   I ask who's in the fireplace
   And you tell me Santa Claus
   The milkman comes in
   He's wearing a derby hat
   Then you ask why I don't live here
   Honey, how come you have to ask me that?

3. Well I asked for something to eat
   I'm hungry as a hog
   So I get brown rice, seaweed,
   And a dirty hot dog
   I've got a hole
   Where my stomach disappeared
   Then you ask why I don't live here
   Honey, I gotta think you're really weird.

4. Your Grandpa's cane
   It turns into a sword
   Your Grandma prays to pictures
   That are pasted on a board
   Ev'rything inside my pockets
   Your uncle steals
   Then you ask why I don't live here
   Honey, I can't believe that you're for real.

5. Well there's fist fights in the kitchen
   They're enough to make me cry
   The mailman comes in
   Even he's gotta take a side
   Even the butler,
   He's got something to prove
   Then you ask why I don't live here
   Honey, how come you don't move?

Outlaw Blues

WORDS AND MUSIC BY BOB DYLAN

1. Ain't it hard to stum-ble and land in some fun-ny la-goon? Ain't it hard

to stum-ble _____ and land in some mud-dy la - goon?

Es- pe-cial-ly when it's nine be-low ze - ro and

N.C.

Repeat 4 times

Three o' clock in the af - ter-noon.

last time fade

2. Ain't gonna hang no picture
Ain't gonna hang no picture frame
Ain't gonna hang no picture
Ain't gonna hang no picture frame
Well, I might look like Robert Ford
But I feel just like a Jesse James.

3. Well I wish I was on some
Australian mountain range
Oh I wish I was on some
Australian mountain range
I got no reason to be there but I
Imagine it would be some kind of change.

4. I got my dark sun glasses
I got for good luck my black tooth
I got my dark sun glasses
I'm carryin' for good luck my black tooth
Don't ask me nothin' about nothin'
I just might tell you the truth.

5. I got a woman in Jackson
I ain't gonna say her name
I got a woman in Jackson
I ain't gonna say her name
She's a brown skin woman, but
I love her just the same.

She Belongs to Me

WORDS AND MUSIC BY BOB DYLAN

1. She's got ev-'ry thing_ she needs She's an art - ist She don't look back

She's got ev-'ry thing_ she needs She's an

art - ist She don't look back   She can take the

dark out of the night-time And __ paint the day-time black.

Repeat 4 times

2. You will start out standing
   Proud to steal her anything she sees
   You will start out standing
   Proud to steal her anything she sees
   But you will wind up peeking through her keyhole
   Down upon your knees.

3. She never stumbles
   She's got no place to fall
   She never stumbles
   She's got no place to fall
   She's nobody's child
   The law can't touch her at all.

4. She wears an Egyptian ring
   That sparkles before she speaks
   She wears an Egyptian ring
   That sparkles before she speaks
   She is a hypnotist collector
   You are a walking antique.

5. Bow down to her on Sunday
   Salute her when her birthday comes
   Bow down to her on Sunday
   Salute her when her birthday comes
   For Halloween give her a trumpet
   And for Christmas, buy her a drum.

The Times They Are A-Changin'

WORDS AND MUSIC BY BOB DYLAN

2. **Come writers and critics**
   Who prophecies with your pen
   And keep your eyes wide
   The chance won't come again.
   And don't speak too soon
   For the wheel's still in spin
   And there's no tellin' who
   That it's namin'
   For the loser now
   Will be later to win
   For the times they are a-changin'.

3. **Come senators, congressmen**
   Please heed the call
   Don't stand in the doorway
   Don't block up the hall.
   For he that gets hurt
   Will be he who has stalled
   There's a battle
   Outside and it's ragin'
   It'll soon shake your windows
   And rattle your walls
   For the times they are a-changin'.

4. **Come mothers and fathers,**
   Throughout the land
   And don't criticize
   What you can't understand.
   Your sons and your daughters
   Are beyond your command
   Your old road is
   Rapidly agin'
   Please get out of the new one
   If you can't lend your hand
   For the times they are a-changin'.

5. **The line it is drawn**
   The curse it is cast
   The slow one now will
   Later be fast.
   As the present now
   Will later be past
   The order is rapidly fadin'
   And the first one now
   Will later be last
   For the times they are a-changin'.

Lay Down Your Weary Tune

WORDS AND MUSIC BY BOB DYLAN

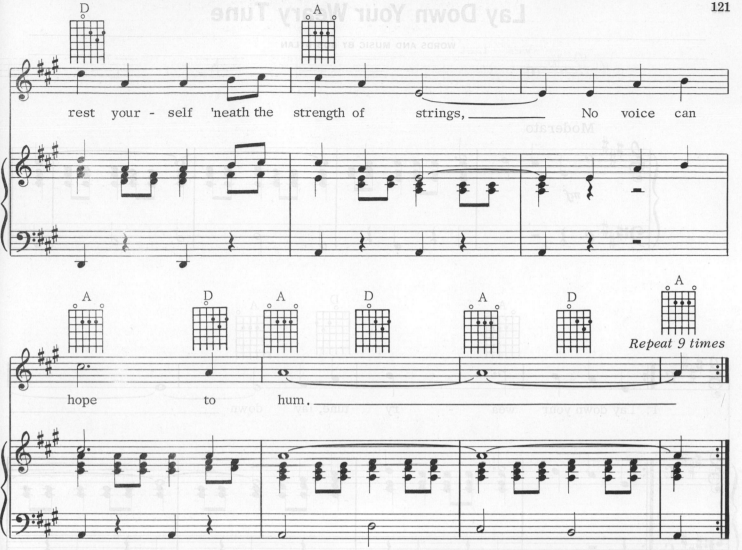

Lay Down Your Weary Tune

WORDS AND MUSIC BY BOB DYLAN

2. Struck by the sounds before the sun,
   I knew the night had gone,
   The morning breeze like a bugle blew
   Against the drums of dawn.

3. Lay down your weary tune, lay down,
   Lay down the song you strum
   And rest yourself 'neath the strength of strings,
   No voice can hope to hum.

4. The ocean wild like an organ played
   The seaweed's wove its strands,
   The crashin' waves like cymbals clashed
   Against the rocks and sands.

5. Lay down your weary tune, lay down,
   Lay down the song you strum
   And rest yourself 'neath the strength of strings,
   No voice can hope to hum.

6. I stood unwound beneath the skies
   And clouds unbound by laws,
   The cryin' rain like a trumpet sang
   And asked for no applause.

7. Lay down your weary tune, lay down,
   Lay down the song you strum
   And rest yourself 'neath the strength of strings,
   No voice can hope to hum.

8. The last of leaves fell from the trees
   And clung to a new love's breast,
   The branches bare like a banjo
   To the winds that listen the best.

9. I gazed down in the river's mirror
   And watched its winding strum
   The water smooth ran like a hymn
   And like a harp did hum.

10. Lay down your weary tune, lay down,
    Lay down the song you strum
    And rest yourself 'neath the strength of strings,
    No voice can hope to hum.

Quit Your Low Down Ways

WORDS AND MUSIC BY BOB DYLAN

2. Well, you can run down to the White House,
   You can gaze at the Capitol Dome, pretty mama,
   You can pound on the President's gate
   But you oughta know by now it's gonna be too late.

REFRAIN

3. Well, you can run down to the desert,
   Throw yourself on the burning sand,
   You can raise up your right hand, pretty mama,
   But you better understand you done lost your one
                               good man.
REFRAIN

4. And you can hitch hike on the highway,
   You can stand all alone by the side of the road,
   You can try to flag a ride back home, pretty mama,
   But you can't ride in my car no more.

REFRAIN

5. Oh, you can read out your Bible,
   You can fall down on your knees, pretty mama,
   And pray to the Lord
   But it ain't gonna do no good.

REFRAIN

Walkin' Down the Line

WORDS AND MUSIC BY BOB DYLAN

Verse 1.

1. I got a heav-y head-ed gal, _____ I got a heav-y head-ed

gal, _____ I got a heav-y head-ed gal, She

ain't a-feel-in' well, When she's bet-ter on-ly time will tell. ___

to Refrain

Verse 2.

2. My mon-ey comes and goes, _____ My mon-ey comes and goes, _____

Who Killed Davey Moore?

WORDS AND MUSIC BY BOB DYLAN

Who Killed Davey Moore?

WORDS AND MUSIC BY BOB DYLAN

Dm

I could-'ve stopped it in the eighth An' may-be kept him from his fate, But the

Gm

crowd would-'ve booed I'm sure At not get-tin' their mon-ey's worth. It's

Gm

too bad he had to go But there was pres-sure on me too, you know. It's

A   Repeat 5 times

It was-n't me that made him fall, No you can't blame me at all''.

REFRAIN:

VERSE 2. "Not us", says the angry crowd,
Whose screams filled the arena loud.
"It's too bad he died that nite
But we just like to see a fight.
We didn't mean for him t' meet his death
We just meant to see some sweat,
There ain't nothin' wrong in that.
It wasn't us that made him fall
No you can't blame us at all".

REFRAIN:

VERSE 3. "Not me", says his manager,
Puffing on a big cigar,
"It's hard to say, it's hard to tell
I always thought that he was well.
It's too bad for his wife an' kids he's dead,
But if he was sick, he should've said.
It wasn't me that made him fall
No you can't blame me at all".

REFRAIN:

VERSE 4. "Not me", says the gambling man,
With his ticket stub still in his hand,
"It wasn't me that knocked him down
My hands never touched him none.
I didn't commit no ugly sin,
Anyway I put money on him to win.
It wasn't me that made him fall
No you can't blame me at all".

REFRAIN:

VERSE 5. "Not me", says the boxing writer,
Pounding print on his old typewriter,
Sayin' "boxing ain't to blame
There's just as much danger in a football game".
Sayin' "fist fighting is here to stay
It's just the old American way.
It wasn't me that made him fall
No you can't blame me at all".

REFRAIN:

VERSE 6. "Not me", says the man whose fists
Laid him low in a cloud of mist,
Who came here from Cuba's door
Where boxing ain't allowed no more.
"I hit him, yes, it's true,
But that's what I am paid to do.
Don't say 'murder', don't say 'kill',
It was destiny, it was God's will".

REFRAIN:

Let Me Die in My Footsteps

WORDS AND MUSIC BY BOB DYLAN

Not too fast

mf

G

1. I will not go down un-der the ground _____ 'Cause
2. There's been ru-mors of war and wars that have been _____ The

G   C

some-bod-y tells me that death's com-in' 'round _____ an' I
mean-ing of life has been lost in the wind _____ and

2. There's been

3. I don't know if I'm smart
   But I think I can see
   When someone is pullin'
   The wool over me
   An' if this war comes
   And death's all around
   Let me die on this land
   'fore I die underground
   Let me die in my footsteps
   Before I go down under the ground

4. There's always been people
   That have to cause fear
   They've been talkin' of the war now
   For many long years
   I have read all their statements
   And I've not said a word
   But now Lawd, God
   Let my poor voice be heard
   Let me die in my footsteps
   Before I go down under the ground

5. If I had rubies
   And riches and crowns
   I'd buy the whole world
   And change things around
   I'd throw all the guns
   And the tanks in the sea
   For they are mistakes
   Of a past history
   Let me die in my footsteps
   Before I go down under the ground

6. Let me drink from the waters
   Where the mountain streams flood
   Let the smell of wild flowers
   Flow free through my blood
   Let me sleep in your meadows
   With the green grassy leaves
   Let me walk down the highway
   With my brother in peace
   Let me die in my footsteps
   Before I go down under the ground

7. Go out in your country
   Where the land meets the sun
   See the craters and the canyons
   Where the waterfalls run
   Nevada, New Mexico, Arizona, Idaho
   Let every state in this union
   Seep down deep in your soul
   And you'll die in your footsteps
   Before you go down under the ground.

Like a Rolling Stone

WORDS AND MUSIC BY BOB DYLAN

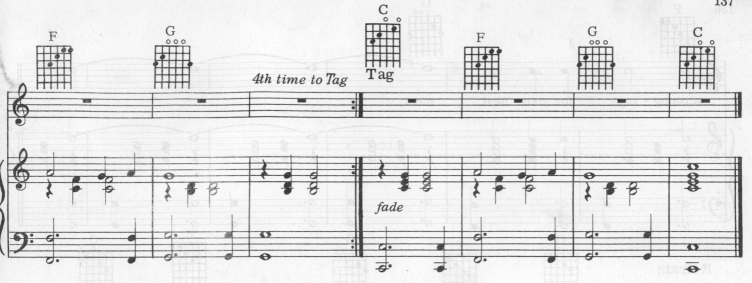

Verse 2. You've gone to the finest school all right Miss Lonely,
But you know you only used to get
Juiced in it.
And nobody's ever taught you how to live on the street
And now you're gonna have to get
Used to it.
You said you'd never compromise
With the mystery tramp, but now you realize
He's not selling any alibis
As you stare into the vacuum of his eyes
And ask him do you want to
Make a deal?

Refrain:

Verse 3. You never turned around to see the frowns on the jugglers and the clowns
When they all come down
And did tricks for you
You never understood that it ain't no good
You shouldn't let other people
Get your kicks for you.
You used to ride on the chrome horse with your diplomat
Who carried on his shoulder a Siamese cat,
Ain't it hard when you discovered that
He really wasn't where it's at
After he took from you everything
He could steal.

Refrain:

Verse 4. Princess on the steeple
And all the pretty people're drinkin', thinkin'
That they got it made.
Exchanging all kinds of precious gifts and things
But you'd better lift your diamond ring,
You'd better pawn it babe,
You used to be so amused
At Napoleon in rags and the language that he used
Go to him now, he calls you, you can't refuse
When you got nothing,you got nothing to lose,
You're invisible now, you got no secrets
To conceal.

Refrain:

recordings of bob dylan's songs

TITLE	ARTIST	LABEL
ALL I REALLY WANT TO DO	BOB DYLAN	Columbia
	The Byrds	Columbia
	Cher	Imperial
	The L. A. Teens	Decca
	The Satans	Decca
	David Rose	MGM
BALLAD IN PLAIN D	BOB DYLAN	Columbia
BALLAD OF HOLLIS BROWN	BOB DYLAN	Columbia
BLACK CROW BLUES	BOB DYLAN	Columbia
BLOWIN' IN THE WIND	BOB DYLAN	Columbia
	The Chad Mitchell Trio	Kapp
	The Harry Simeone Chorale	Mercury
	Jerry Jackson	Kapp
	Johnny Maddox	Dot
	The Millburnaires '63	Battle
	Peter, Paul & Mary	Warner Bros.
	The Staples Singers	Riverside
	Martin Yarbrough	Argo
	Martin Denny	Liberty
	Arthur Lyman	Hi-Fidelity
	Bob Harter	Liberty
	The Kingston Trio	Capitol
	Jackie DeShannon	Liberty
	Dennis & Rogers	Crescendo
	Odetta	RCA Victor
	The Folkniks	Hi-Fidelity
	The Troubador Singers	Vee Jay
	Rod McKuen & Horizon Singers	Vee Jay
	The Village Stompers	Columbia
	Les & Larry Elgart	Columbia
	Leroy Holmes Singers	United Artists
	Bobby Darin	Capitol
	Spike Jones	Liberty
	Percy Faith	Columbia
	The Folkswingers	Pacific
	Lena Horne	20th Century Fox
	The Sidewalk Swingers	Warner Bros.
	Bill Justis	Mercury
	Johnny Tillotson	MGM
	Eddy Arnold	RCA Victor
	The Banjo Barons	Columbia
	Bradley Wayne	Vee Jay
	Greenwich Village Migrants	Cameo
	Living Guitars	Camden
	Bud Shank	Pacific
	Glen Campbell	Capitol
	Brian Hyland	Mercury
	Stan Getz	Verve
	Johnny Mann	Liberty
	The Browns	RCA Victor
	Ray Bryant	Sue
	Linda Mason	Rik
	Duke Ellington	Reprise
	Trini Lopez	Reprise
	Dick Dale & His Del Tones	Capitol
	The Castaway Strings	Vee Jay
	Sam Cooke	Tracey

TITLE	ARTIST	LABEL
	Bobby Richards	Capitol
	Walter Jackson	Epic
	Golden Gate Strings	Epic
	The Canada Sweethearts	A & M
	Marlene Dietrich	Capitol
	Bobby Bare	RCA Victor
	Cliff Davis	Columbia
	The Shenandoah Trio	Dot
	Cher	Imperial
BOB DYLAN'S DREAM	BOB DYLAN	Columbia
BOB DYLAN'S 115th DREAM	BOB DYLAN	Columbia
BOOTS OF SPANISH LEATHER	BOB DYLAN	Columbia
	Linda Mason	Rik
CHIMES OF FREEDOM	BOB DYLAN	Columbia
	The Byrds	Columbia
	Dino, Desi & Billy	Reprise
DON'T THINK TWICE, IT'S ALL RIGHT	BOB DYLAN	Columbia
	The New World Singers	Atlantic
	The Harry Simeone Chorale	Mercury
	Jackie DeShannon	Liberty
	Peter, Paul & Mary	Warner Bros.
	The Folkniks	Hi-Fidelity
	Joan Baez	Vanguard
	Bobby Darin	Capitol
	The Sidewalk Swingers	Warner Bros.
	The Folkswingers	Pacific
	Brian Hyland	ABC Paramount
	Julie Felix	London
	The Golden Gate Strings	Epic
	Lawrence Welk	Dot
	The Transients	Vee Jay
	Dick & DeeDee	Warner Bros.
	Bradley Wayne	Vee Jay
	Greenwich Village Migrants	Cameo
	Village Stompers	Epic
	Bud Shank	Pacific
	Walter Raim	Liberty
	Johnny Mann	Liberty
	All Night Singers	Warner Bros.
	Linda Mason	Rik
	The Brothers Four	Columbia
	Marc Ellington	Tap On Tap
	Trini Lopez	Reprise
	Johnny Cash	Columbia
	Odetta	RCA Victor
	The Castaway Strings	Vee Jay
	Jose Feliciano	RCA Victor
	Bobby Bare	RCA Victor
	The Seekers	Capitol
	The Shenandoah Trio	Dot
	Cher	Imperial
	Randy Boone	Decca
ETERNAL CIRCLE	BOB DYLAN	Columbia
FAREWELL	BOB DYLAN	Columbia
	Judy Collins	Elektra
	Anita Carter	Mercury
	Modern Folk Quartet	Warner Bros.
	The Limeliters	RCA Victor
	Linda Mason	Rik
	The Kingston Trio	Decca
	Carter Family	Columbia
	Joe & Eddie	Crescendo
	Martin Yarbrough	Argo

TITLE	ARTIST	LABEL
	Golden Gate Strings	Epic
GATES OF EDEN, THE	BOB DYLAN	Columbia
GIRL OF THE NORTH COUNTRY	BOB DYLAN	Columbia
	Baytown Singers	MGM
	Hamilton Camp	Elektra
HARD RAIN'S A GONNA FALL, A	BOB DYLAN	Columbia
	Pete Seeger	Columbia
	Dick Weissman	Capitol
	Linda Mason	Rik
	Golden Gate Strings	Epic
I DON'T BELIEVE YOU	BOB DYLAN	Columbia
	Skip Battyn	RCA Victor
	Two Guys from Boston	Scepter
	The Turtles	White Whale
IT AIN'T ME, BABE	BOB DYLAN	Columbia
	Joan Baez	Vanguard
	Johnny Cash	Columbia
	Marc Ellington	On Tap
	Golden Gate Strings	Epic
	The Turtles	White Whale
	Joe & Eddie	Crescendo
	The Safaris	Decca
	David Jones	Colpix
	Dino, Desi & Billy	Reprise
IT'S ALL OVER NOW, BABY BLUE	BOB DYLAN	Columbia
	Golden Gate Strings	Epic
	The Devons	Decca
	Leroy Van Dyke	Warner Bros.
IT'S ALRIGHT MA (I'm Only Bleeding)	BOB DYLAN	Columbia
LAY DOWN YOUR WEARY TUNE	Bill Henderson	Verve
LET ME DIE IN MY FOOTSTEPS	BOB DYLAN	Columbia
LIKE A ROLLING STONE	BOB DYLAN	Columbia
	The Safaris	Decca
	The Turtles	White Whale
	Dino, Desi & Billy	Reprise
LOVE MINUS ZERO/NO LIMIT	BOB DYLAN	Columbia
	The Turtles	White Whale
MAGGIE'S FARM	BOB DYLAN	Columbia
	Solomon Burke	Atlantic
MASTERS OF WAR	BOB DYLAN	Columbia
	Judy Collins	Elektra
	Ronnie Gilbert	Mercury
	Linda Mason	Rik
	Odetta	RCA Victor
	The Talismen	World Artists
	Julie Felix	London
	Pete Seeger	Columbia
MR. TAMBOURINE MAN	BOB DYLAN	Columbia
	Odetta	RCA Victor
	Chad & Jeremy	Columbia
	The Brothers Four	Columbia
	The Byrds	Columbia
	Golden Gate Strings	Epic
	The Village Stompers	Columbia
	The Chipmunks	Liberty
	Gerry Mulligan	Limelight
	Dino, Desi & Billy	Reprise
	David Rose	MGM
	Glen Campbell	Capitol

TITLE	ARTIST	LABEL
	Johnny Mann	Liberty
MOTORPSYCHO NIGHTMARE	BOB DYLAN	Columbia
MY BACK PAGES	BOB DYLAN	Columbia
NORTH COUNTRY BLUES	BOB DYLAN	Columbia
ONLY A PAWN IN THEIR GAME	BOB DYLAN	Columbia
ON THE ROAD AGAIN	BOB DYLAN	Columbia
OUTLAW BLUES	BOB DYLAN	Columbia
OXFORD TOWN	BOB DYLAN	Columbia
PATHS OF VICTORY	Hamilton Camp Odetta	Elektra RCA Victor
QUIT YOUR LOW DOWN WAYS	BOB DYLAN Peter, Paul & Mary Bud Shank	Columbia Warner Bros. Pacific
SEVEN CURSES	BOB DYLAN	Columbia
SHE BELONGS TO ME	BOB DYLAN	Columbia
SPANISH HARLEM INCIDENT	BOB DYLAN The Byrds	Columbia Columbia
SUBTERRANEAN HOMESICK BLUES	BOB DYLAN Golden Gate Strings	Columbia Epic
THE TIMES THEY ARE A-CHANGIN'	BOB DYLAN Peter, Paul & Mary Peter Antell Simon & Garfunkel Odetta Golden Gate Strings Ian Campbell Folk Group The Seekers	Columbia Warner Bros. Bounty Columbia RCA Victor Epic 20th Century Fox Capitol
TOMORROW IS A LONG TIME	BOB DYLAN Ian & Sylvia Bud & Travis The Brothers Four Carol Hedin Linda Mason Hamilton Camp Odetta Golden Gate Strings	Columbia Vanguard Liberty Columbia Franc Rik Elektra RCA Victor Epic
TO RAMONA	BOB DYLAN The Hondells	Columbia Mercury
WALKING DOWN THE LINE	Jackie DeShannon Glen Campbell Al Caiola Hamilton Camp Odetta Joe & Eddie	Liberty Capitol United Artist Elektra RCA Victor Crescendo
WHEN THE SHIP COMES IN	BOB DYLAN Peter, Paul & Mary Golden Gate Strings	Columbia Warner Bros. Epic
WHO KILLED DAVEY MOORE?	Linda Mason Pete Seeger The New Wine Singers	Rik Columbia Bell
WITH GOD ON OUR SIDE	BOB DYLAN Joan Baez Linda Mason Chad Mitchell Trio Odetta Golden Gate Strings	Columbia Vanguard Rik Mercury RCA Victor Epic

Chord diagrams for Ukulele, Five String Banjo, Tenor Banjo and Baritone Ukulele used in this Folio.

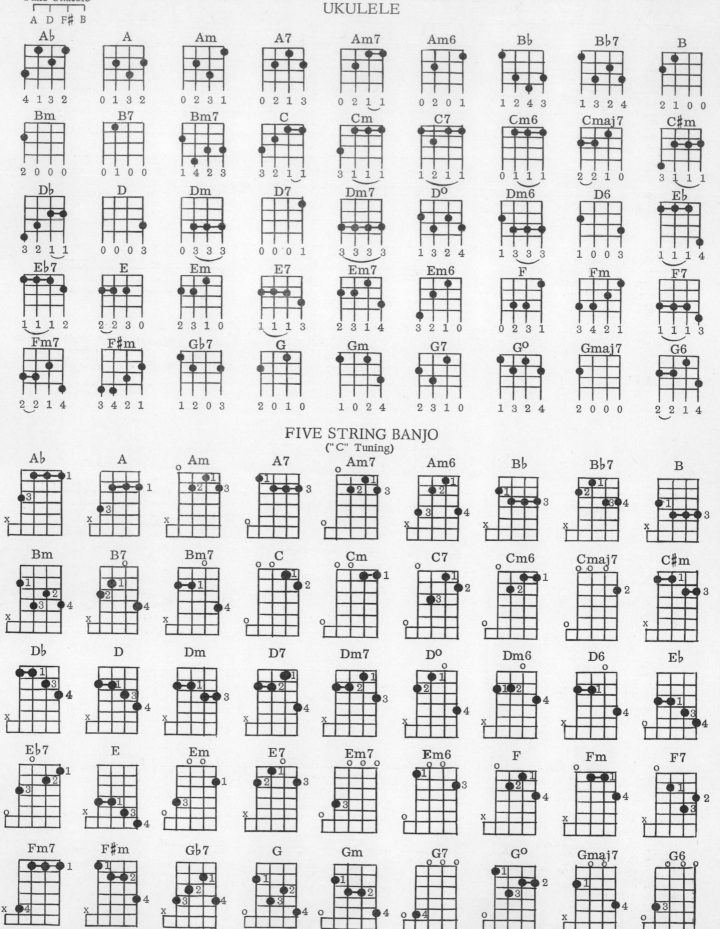

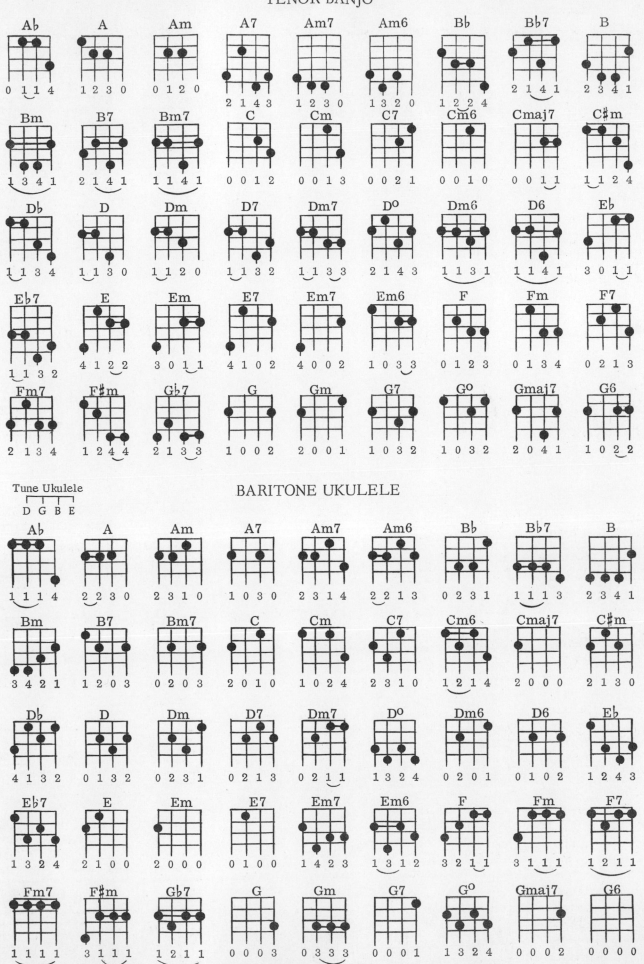